Health and Safety
Executive

Display Screen

Health and Safety (Display Screen Equipment) Regulations

Guidance on Regulations

L26

London: HMSO

© Crown copyright 1992
Applications for reproduction should be made to
HMSO
First published 1992

ISBN 0 11 886331 2

Enquiries regarding this or any other HSE
publications should be made to the HSE
Information Centre at the following address:

HSE Information Centre
Broad Lane
Sheffield
S3 7HQ
Tel: (0742) 892345
Fax: (0742) 892333

Contents

Introduction

1   This booklet gives guidance on the Health and Safety (Display Screen Equipment) Regulations 1992, which come into force on 1 January 1993. The Regulations implement a European directive, No. 90/270/EEC of 29 May 1990, on minimum safety and health requirements for work with display screen equipment.

2   The guidance covers these Regulations only but employers should ensure that they also comply with general duties placed on them by other health and safety legislation, particularly their general obligations under the Health and Safety at Work etc Act 1974 (the HSW Act) and associated legislation. This includes three new sets of Regulations relevant to all or most workplaces - the Management of Health and Safety at Work Regulations 1992, the Workplace (Health, Safety and Welfare) Regulations 1992, and the Provision and Use of Work Equipment Regulations 1992. These are described in the box below.

New general Regulations

Management of Health and Safety at Work Regulations

These Regulations set out broad general duties which apply to almost all kinds of work. They will require employers to:

- assess the risk to the health and safety of their employees and to anyone else who may be affected by their activity, so that the necessary preventive and protective measures can be identified;

- make arrangements for putting into practice the health and safety measures that follow from the risk assessment, covering planning, organisation, control, monitoring and review, in other words, the management of health and safety;

- provide appropriate health surveillance of employees where necessary;

- appoint competent people to help devise and apply the measures needed to comply with employers' duties under health and safety law;

- set up emergency procedures;

- give employees information about health and safety matters;

- co-operate with any other employers who share a work site;

- provide information to people working in their undertaking who are not their employees;

- make sure that employees have adequate health and safety training and are capable enough at their jobs to avoid risk; and

- give some particular health and safety information to temporary workers, to meet their special needs.

The Regulations will also:

- place duties on employees to follow health and safety instructions and report danger; and

- extend the current law which requires employers to consult employees' safety representatives and provide facilities for them. Consultation must now take place on such matters as the introduction of measures that may substantially affect health and safety; the arrangements for appointing competent persons; health and safety information and training required by law; and health and safety aspects of new technology being introduced to the workplace.

Provision and Use of Work Equipment Regulations

These Regulations are designed to pull together and tidy up the laws governing equipment used at work. Instead of piecemeal legislation covering particular kinds of equipment in different industries, they place general duties on employers and list minimum requirements for work equipment to deal with selected hazards whatever the industry.

'Work equipment' is broadly defined to include everything from a hand tool, through machines of all kinds, to a complete plant such as refinery. It therefore includes display screen equipment. 'Use' includes starting, stopping, programming, setting, transporting, repairing, modifying, maintaining, servicing and cleaning.

The general duties will require employers to:

- take into account the working conditions and risks in the workplace when selecting equipment;

- make sure that equipment is suitable for the use that will be made of it and that it is properly maintained; and

- give adequate information, instruction and training.

Specific requirements cover:

- protection from dangerous parts of machinery (replacing the current law on this);

- maintenance operations;

- danger caused by other specified hazards;

- parts and materials at high or very low temperatures;

- control systems and controls;

- isolation of equipment from power sources;

- stability of equipment;

- lighting; and

- warnings and markings.

Workplace (Health, Safety and Welfare) Regulations

These Regulations will replace a total of 38 pieces of older law, including parts of the Factories Act 1961 and the Offices, Shops and Railway Premises Act 1963. They cover many aspects of health, safety and welfare in the workplace and will apply to all places of work except:

- means of transport;

- construction sites;

- sites where extraction of mineral resources or exploration for them is carried out; and

- fishing boats.

Workplaces on agricultural or forestry land away from main buildings are also exempted from most requirements.

The Regulations set general requirements in four broad areas:

- *Working environment*, including: temperature; ventilation; lighting including emergency lighting; room dimensions; suitability of workstations and seating; and outdoor workstations (eg weather protection).

- *Safety*, including: safe passage of pedestrians and vehicles; windows and skylights (safe opening, closing and cleaning); glazed doors and partitions (use of safe material and marking); doors, gates and escalators (safety devices); floors (their construction, and obstructions and slipping and tripping hazards); falls from heights and into dangerous substances; and falling objects.

- *Facilities*, including: toilets; washing, eating and changing facilities; clothing storage; seating; rest areas (and arrangements in them for non-smokers); and rest facilities for pregnant women and nursing mothers.

- *Housekeeping*, including: maintenance of workplace, equipment and facilities; cleanliness; and removal of waste materials.

3   There are some overlaps between general and specific legislation. Where broadly applicable legislation such as the Regulations described in the box imposes a general duty similar to a more specific one in the Display Screen Equipment Regulations - for example the risk assessments required by the Management of Health and Safety at Work Regulations (MHSWR) - the legal requirement is to comply with **both** the more specific and the general duty. However, this should not give rise to any difficulty in practice. For example, in display screen work:

(a)   carrying out the suitable and sufficient analysis of workstations and risk assessment required by Regulation 2 (see paragraphs 19-35 below) will also satisfy the MHSWR requirement for risk assessment as far as those workstations are concerned;

(b)   ensuring that the requirements for lighting, reflections and glare in the schedule to the Display Screen Regulations are met (see Annex A, paragraphs 20-24) will also satisfy the requirements for suitable and sufficient lighting in the Provision and Use of Work Equipment Regulations and the Workplace (Health, Safety and Welfare) Regulations, as far as the display screen workstations are concerned.

In these examples, as in other matters, the employer would still have to take other appropriate steps to ensure that the general duties (to carry out risk assessments, ensure suitable lighting etc) were complied with in any other parts of his undertaking where display screen work is not carried out.

Structure of this booklet

4   The guidance below gives information, explanation or advice in relation to specific requirements of the Regulations, which are printed in italics at the start of each relevant part of the guidance. Where the Regulations are self-explanatory no comment is offered.

Regulation 1

Citation, commencement, interpretation and application

Regulation

(1)   These Regulations may be cited as the Health and Safety (Display Screen Equipment) Regulations 1992 and shall come into force on 1 January 1993.

(2)   In these Regulations -

(a)   "display screen equipment" means any alphanumeric or graphic display screen, regardless of the display process involved;

(b)   "operator" means a self-employed person who habitually uses display screen equipment as a significant part of his normal work;

(c)   "use" means use for or in connection with work;

(d)   "user" means an employee who habitually uses display screen equipment as a significant part of his normal work; and

(e)   "workstation" means an assembly comprising -

(i)   display screen equipment (whether provided with software determining the interface between the equipment and its operator or user, a keyboard or any other input device),

(ii)   any optional accessories to the display screen equipment,

(iii)   any disk drive, telephone, modem, printer, document holder, work chair, work desk, work surface or other item peripheral to the display screen equipment, and

(iv)   the immediate work environment around the display screen equipment.

1(1)-(3)

(3) Any reference in these Regulations to -

(a) a numbered regulation is a reference to the regulation in these Regulations so numbered; or

(b) a numbered paragraph is a reference to the paragraph so numbered in the regulation in which the reference appears.

5   The definitions of "display screen equipment", "workstation", "user" and "operator" determine whether or not the Regulations apply in a particular situation.

Which display screen equipment is covered?

6   With a few exceptions (see paragraphs 14-18), the definition of display screen equipment at Regulation 1(2)(a) covers both conventional (cathode ray tube) display screens and other display processes such as liquid crystal displays, and other emerging technologies. Display screens mainly used to display line drawings, graphs, charts or computer generated graphics are included, but screens whose **main** use is to show television or film pictures are not. Judgements about mixed media workstations will be needed to establish the main use of the screen; if this is to display text, numbers and/or graphics, it is within the scope of the Regulations. The definition is not limited to typical office visual display terminals but covers, for example, non-electronic display systems such as microfiche. Process control screens are also covered in principle (where there are "users" - see below) although certain requirements may not apply (see paragraphs 38-40).

7   The use of display screen equipment not covered by these Regulations is still subject to other, general health and safety legislation; see paragraphs 2 and 3 above. For example, there are requirements for suitable and sufficient lighting in the Provision and Use of Work Equipment Regulations 1992; and there are general requirements for risk assessment and provision of training and information in the Management of Health and Safety at Work Regulations 1992. Where a display screen is in use but the Display Screen Equipment Regulations do not apply, the assessment of risks and measures taken to control them should take account of ergonomic factors applicable to display screen work. This is also true where these Regulations do not apply because the display screen is not used by a "user" - see below.

Who is a display screen user or operator?

8   The Regulations are for the protection of people - employees and self-employed - who habitually use display screen equipment for the purposes of an employer's undertaking as a significant part of their normal work.

9   Regulation 1(2)(d) defines the **employees** who are covered as "users" and all the Regulations apply to protect them, as specified, whether they are required to work:

-    at their own employer's workstation;

-    at a workstation at home;

-    at another employer's workstation. In this case that other employer must comply with Regulations 2, 3, 4, 6 (2) and 7, and their own employer with Regulations 5 and 6 (1), as is specified in the Regulations concerned.

5

Regulations 2, 3 and 7 apply, as specified, to protect self-employed people who work at the client employer's workstation and whose use of display screen equipment is such that they would be users if employed. They are defined in Regulation 1(2)(b) as "operators" for the purposes of the Regulations.

10   Employers must therefore decide which of their employees are display screen users and whether they also make use of other users (employed by other employers) or of operators. Workers who do not input or extract information by means of display screen equipment need not be regarded as users or operators in this context - for example many of those engaged in manufacture, sales, maintenance or the cleaning of display screen equipment. Whether or not those involved in display screen work are users or operators depends on the nature and extent of their use of the equipment.

11   The need for such a definition stems from the fact that possible hazards associated with display screen use are mainly those leading to musculoskeletal problems, visual fatigue and stress (see paragraph 19 below and Annex B). The likelihood of experiencing these is related mainly to the frequency, duration, intensity and pace of spells of continuous use of the display screen equipment, allied to other factors, such as the amount of discretion the person has over the extent and methods of display screen use. The combination of factors which give rise to risks makes it impossible to lay down hard and fast rules (eg based on set hours' usage per day or week) about who should be classified as a user or operator.

12   In some cases it will be clear that use of display screen equipment is more or less continuous on most days and the individuals concerned should be regarded as users or operators. This will include the majority of those whose job mainly involves, for example, display screen based data input or sales and order processing. Where use is less continuous or frequent, other factors connected with the job must be assessed. It will generally be appropriate to classify the person concerned as a user or operator if most or all of the following criteria apply:

(a)   the individual depends on the use of display screen equipment to do the job, as alternative means are not readily available for achieving the same results;

(b)   the individual has no discretion as to use or non-use of the display screen equipment;

(c)   the individual needs significant training and/or particular skills in the use of display screen equipment to do the job;

(d)   the individual normally uses display screen equipment for continuous spells of an hour or more at a time;

(e)   the individual uses display screen equipment in this way more or less daily;

(f)   fast transfer of information between the user and screen is an important requirement of the job;

(g)   the performance requirements of the system demand high levels of attention and concentration by the user, for example, where the consequences of error may be critical.

Some examples to illustrate these factors are included in the box. This is **not** an exhaustive list of display screen jobs, but a list of examples chosen to illuminate the above criteria.

Who is a display screen user?

Some examples

Definite display screen users

Word processing pool worker employed on full time text input using dedicated display screen equipment. A mix of checking from screen, keyboard input and formatting. Some change of posture involved in collecting work, operating printer etc. Often five hours in total on the work itself with a lunch break and at least two breaks morning and afternoon. Part-time workers, required to work fewer hours but spending all or most of their working time on this kind of work would also be included.

Secretary or typist who uses a dedicated word processing system and laser printer. Word processing of reports, memos, letters from manuscript and dictation, combined with electronic mail. Some variation in workload with a concomitant degree of control over scheduling throughout the day. Typically around two or three hours daily.

Data Input Operator employed full time on continuous processing of invoices. Predominantly numeric input using numeric key pad. Other keystroke monitoring with associated bonus system. Part-timers, or other staff temporarily assigned to this work to deal with peak workloads, would be definite "users" while spending all or most of their working time on these duties.

News sub-editor making use of display screen equipment more or less continuously with peak workloads. Some text input to abridge/precis stories, but mainly scanning copy for fact, punctuation, grammar and size.

Journalist whose pattern of work may be variable but includes substantial use of display screen equipment. Information collected by field or telephone interviews (which may involve use of a portable computer) followed by, typically, several hours text input while working on a story. Work likely to be characterised by deadlines and interruptions. Some days may contain periods of less intense work but with more prolonged keyboard text entry and composition.

Tele-Sales/customer complaints/accounts enquiry/directory enquiry operator employed on mainly full-time display screen use while taking telephone enquiries from customers/public.

Air traffic controller whose main task is monitoring of purpose designed screens for air traffic movements combined with communication with air crew on navigation etc. High visual and mental workload. Shift work.

Financial dealer using a dedicated workstation typically with multiple display screens. Variable/unpredictable workload. Often highly stressful situations with information overload. Often long hours.

Graphic designer working on multimedia applications. Intensive scrutiny of images at high resolution. Large screens. Page make-up. Multiple input devices. Colour systems critical.

Librarian carrying out intensive text input on dedicated equipment to add to information held on databases; accessing and checking on records held on databases, eg bibliographic and lending references; creating summaries and reports, combining data held on the equipment and new copy inputted into the system. Display screen work either intensive throughout the day on most days, or more intermittent but still forming at least half of the librarian's total working time.

Possible display screen users - depending on the circumstances

The following are examples of jobs whose occupants may or may not be designated as display screen users, depending on circumstances. In reaching a decision, employers will need to judge the relative importance of different aspects of the work, weighing these against the factors discussed in paragraph 12 and bearing in mind the risks to which the job-holder may be exposed. If there is doubt over whether an individual is a display screen worker, carrying out a risk assessment (see Regulation 2) should help in reaching a decision.

Scientist/technical adviser having use of dedicated display screen equipment. Word processing of a few letters/memos per day. Monitoring of electronic mail for a short period, average 10 minutes, on most days. At irregular intervals, uses display screen equipment intensively for data analysis of research results.

Discussion: This scientist's daily use of display screen equipment is relatively brief, non-intense and he or she would have a good deal of discretion over when and how the equipment was used. Judged against this daily use, he or she would not be a "user". However, this decision might be reversed if the periods of use for analysis of research results were at all frequent, of long duration and intensive.

Client manager in a large management accounting consultancy. Dedicated display screen equipment on desk. Daily scanning and transmitting of electronic mail. Typically $1^1/_2$-2 hours daily.

Discussion: Whether or not this manager is a user will depend on the extent and nature of his or her use of electronic mail. For example, how continuous is use of the screen and/or keyboard during each period of use; is there discretion as to the extent of use of electronic mail; how long is the total daily use?

Building society customer support officer with shared use of office, desk and display screen workstation. Display screen equipment used during interviews with clients to interrogate HQ database to obtain customer details, transactions etc.

Discussion: Decision will be influenced by what proportion of the individual worker's time is spent using the display screen equipment; are there any prolonged and/or intensive periods of use; and what are the consequences of errors (this factor may be relevant if the job involves inputting financial data as well as searching a database).

Airline check-in clerk whose workload in job as a whole varies during day, with occasional peaks of intensive work as flight times get near. Use of display screen equipment follows a predictable pattern; typically, used as part of most transactions but may not be a significant proportion of total working time.

Discussion: There needs to be consideration of how equipment is used and for what purpose. Is the display screen used during most parts of the check-in process or only a few of them? Is the workload of transactions high? What proportion of each transaction involves viewing the screen or keying in data? Is interaction with the screen rushed and intensive? What are the consequences of errors?

Community care worker using a portable computer to make notes during and/or following interviews or visits in the field.

Discussion: Decisions on whether or not those using laptops are "users" need to be made on the same basis as if they were using non-portable equipment. While some of the specific minimum requirements in the Schedule may not be applicable to portables in prolonged use, as the inherent characteristics of the task may rule them out, it is important that such work is properly assessed, that users are trained, and that measures are taken to control risks.

Receptionist whose job involves frequent use of display screen equipment, for example to check or enter details of each visitor and/or provide them with information.

Discussion: The nature, frequency and duration of periods of display screen work need to be assessed. Some, perhaps most, receptionists would not be users, if most of their work consists of face to face contact and/or phone calls, with a display screen only being used occasionally - see below.

Definitely not display screen users

Senior manager in a large organisation using display screen for occasional monitoring of state of markets or other data, or more frequent but brief enquiries. Low dependency, high control.

Senior manager using display screen equipment at month end for generation/ manipulation of financial statistics for board presentation.

Receptionist if work is mainly concerned with customer/public interaction, with the possibilities of interrogating display screen occasionally for limited purposes such as obtaining details of the organisation (telephone numbers, location etc).

13   The following table shows how the criteria in paragraph 12 relate to the job examples in the box.

Application of "user" criteria to particular jobs

CATEGORY	Job	(a) Dependency	(b) Discretion	(c) Significant training	(d) Prolonged spells > 1 hr	(e) Daily use	(f) Fast information transfer	(g) Criticality of errors
DEFINITELY USERS	Word processing	H	L	Yes	Frequent	Yes	Yes	M
	Secretary	M-H	M	Yes	"	Yes	Yes	M
	Data input	H	L	Yes	"	Yes	Yes	M
	Sub editor	H	L	Yes	"	Yes	Yes	M
	Journalist	M-H	M	Yes	"	Yes	Yes	L
	Tele-sales etc	H	L	Yes	"	Yes	Maybe (paced by incoming calls)	M
	Air traffic control	H	L	Yes	"	Yes	Yes	H
	Financial dealer	H	M	Yes	"	Yes	Yes	H
	Graphic designer	M-H	L	Yes	"	Yes	Maybe	M
	Librarian	H	L	Yes	Variable	Yes	Yes	M
MAY BE USERS	Client manager	M-H	H	No	1 per day	Yes	No	M
	Scientist	L-H	H	No	1 per day	Yes	No	M
	Building society officer	M	M-H	No	Occasional	Yes	No	M
	Airline check-in	M-H	L	Yes	Infrequent	Yes	Variable	M
	Community care	L-H	L-H	No	Infrequent	Maybe	Variable	M
	Receptionist 1	M	M	Yes	Infrequent	Yes	Maybe	M
NOT USERS	Senior manager 1	L-M	H	No	Infrequent	Yes	No	M
	Senior manager 2	L-M	H	No	Infrequent	No	No	M
	Receptionist 2	L-M	H	No	Infrequent	No	No	L

KEY

H = High
M = Medium
L = Low

Application

(4) Nothing in these Regulations shall apply to or in relation to -

(a) drivers' cabs or control cabs for vehicles or machinery;

(b) display screen equipment on board a means of transport;

(c) display screen equipment mainly intended for public operation;

(d) portable systems not in prolonged use;

(e) calculators, cash registers or any equipment having a small data or measurement display required for direct use of the equipment; or

(f) window typewriters.

14   Where any of the exclusions in Regulation 1(4) are operative, none of the specific duties in the Regulations apply to or in connection with the use of the equipment concerned. However, the proviso at paragraph 7 above applies here too. Employers should still ensure that, so far as is reasonably practicable, the health and safety of those using the equipment are not put at risk. The general duties on employers and others under the Health and Safety at Work etc Act 1974, and other general health and safety legislation (see paragraphs 2 and 3), are still applicable and particular attention should be paid to ergonomics in this context.

15   The exclusion in Regulation 1(4)(c) is for display screen equipment mainly provided for short-term operation by the general public, such as cashpoint machines at banks and microfiche readers and computer terminals in public libraries. It does not extend to display screen equipment available for operation by the public but mainly provided for use by users.

16   Portable display screen equipment (such as laptop computers) comes under the exclusion in Regulation 1(4)(d) above only if it is not in prolonged use. While there are no hard and fast rules on what constitutes "prolonged" use, portable equipment that is habitually in use by a display screen user for a significant part of his or her normal work, as explained in paragraphs 11-13 above, should be regarded as covered by the Regulations. While some of the specific minimum requirements in the Schedule may not be applicable to portables in prolonged use, employers should still ensure that such work is assessed and measures taken to control risks.

17   The exclusion in Regulation 1(4)(e) for small data or measurement displays is there because such displays are usually not intensively monitored by workers for long continuous spells. This exclusion covers, for example, much scientific and medical equipment, such as cardiac monitors, oscilloscopes, and instruments with small displays showing a series of digits.

18   The exclusion in Regulation 1(4)(f) is for window typewriters having a small display showing no more than a few lines of text.

Analysis of workstations to assess and reduce risks

(1)   Every employer shall perform a suitable and sufficient analysis of those workstations which –

(a)   (regardless of who has provided them) are used for the purposes of his undertaking by users; or

(b)   have been provided by him and are used for the purposes of his undertaking by operators,

for the purpose of assessing the health and safety risks to which those persons are exposed in consequence of that use.

(2)   Any assessment made by an employer in pursuance of paragraph (1) shall be reviewed by him if -

(a)   there is reason to suspect that it is no longer valid; or

(b)   there has been a significant change in the matters to which it relates;

and where as a result of any such review changes to an assessment are required, the employer concerned shall make them.

(3)   The employer shall reduce the risks identified in consequence of an assessment to the lowest extent reasonably practicable.

(4)   The reference in paragraph (3) to "an assessment" is a reference to an assessment made by the employer concerned in pursuance of paragraph (1) and changed by him where necessary in pursuance of paragraph (2).

19   Possible risks which have been associated with display screen equipment work are summarised at Annex B. The principal risks relate to physical (musculoskeletal) problems, visual fatigue and mental stress. These are not unique to display screen work nor an inevitable consequence of it, and indeed research shows that the risk to the individual user from typical display screen work is low. However, in display screen work as in other types of work, ill health can result from poor work organisation, working environment, job design and posture, and from inappropriate working methods. As discussed in Annex B, some types of display screen work have been associated with chronic musculoskeletal disorders. While surveys indicate that only a very small proportion of display screen workers are likely to be involved, the number of cases may still be significant as display screen workers are so numerous. All the known health problems that may be associated with display screen work can be prevented altogether by good design of the workplace and the job, and by worker training and consultation.

20   Employers will need to assess the extent to which any of the above risks arise for display screen workers using their workstations who are:

-    users employed by them;

-    users employed by others (eg agency employed "temps");

-    operators, ie self-employed contractors who would be classified as users if they were employees (eg self-employed agency "temps", self-employed journalists).

Individual workstations used by any of these people will need to be analysed and risks assessed. If employers require their employees to use workstations at home, these too will need to be assessed (see paragraph 26 below).

If there is doubt whether any individual is a user or operator, carrying out a risk assessment should help in reaching a decision.

Suitable and sufficient analysis and risk assessment

21   Risk assessment should first identify any hazards and then evaluate risks and their extent. A **hazard** is something with the potential to cause harm; **risk** expresses the likelihood that the harm from a particular hazard is realised. The **extent of the risk** takes into account the number of people who might be exposed to a risk and the consequences for them. Analysis of display screen workstations should include a check for the presence of desirable features as well as making sure that bad points have been eliminated. In general, the risks outlined above will arise when the work, workplace and work environment do not take account of worker requirements. Since any risks to health may arise from a combination of risk factors, a suitable and sufficient analysis should:

(a)   be systematic - including investigation of non-obvious causes of problems. For example, poor posture may be a response to screen reflections or glare, rather than poor furniture;

(b)   be appropriate to the likely degree of risk. This will largely depend on the duration, intensity or difficulty of the work undertaken, for example the need for prolonged high concentration because of particular performance requirements;

(c)   be comprehensive, covering organisational, job, workplace and individual factors;

(d)   incorporate information provided by both employer and worker.

The form of the assessment

22   In the simplest and most obvious cases which can be easily repeated and explained at any time an assessment need not be recorded. This might be the case, for example, if no significant risks are indicated and no individual user or operator is identified as being especially at risk. Assessments of short-term or temporary workstations may also not need to be recorded, unless risks are significant. However, in most other cases assessments need to be recorded and kept readily accessible to ensure continuity and accuracy of knowledge among those who may need to know the results (eg where risk reduction measures have yet to be completed). Recorded assessments need not necessarily be a 'paper and pencil' record but could be stored electronically.

23   Information provided by users is an essential part of an assessment. A useful way of obtaining this can be through an ergonomic checklist, which should preferably be completed by users. Other approaches are also possible. For example, more objective elements of the analysis (eg nature of work, chair adjustability, keyboard characteristics etc) could be assessed generically in respect of particular types of equipment or groups of worker. Other aspects of workstations would still need to be assessed individually through information collected from users, but this could then be restricted to subjective factors (eg relating to comfort). **Whatever type of checklist is used, employers should ensure workers have received the necessary training before being asked to complete one.**

13

24   The form of the assessment needs to be appropriate to the nature of the tasks undertaken and the complexity of the workstation. For many office tasks the assessment can be a judgement based on responses to the checklist. Where particular risks are apparent, however, and for complex situations, eg where safety of others is a critical factor, a more detailed assessment may be appropriate. This could include, for example, a task analysis where particular job stresses had been identified, recording of posture, physical measurement of workstations; or quantitative surveys of lighting and glare.

Shared workstations

25   Where one workstation is used by more than one worker, whether simultaneously or in shifts, it should be analysed and assessed in relation to all those covered by the Regulations (see paragraph 9 above).

Assessment of risks to homeworkers

26   If a display screen user (ie an employee) is required by his or her employer to work at home, whether or not the workstation is provided in whole or part by the employer, the risks must be assessed. An ergonomic checklist which the homeworker completes and submits to the employer for assessment is the most practicable means. The assessment will need to cover any need for extra or special training and information provision for homeworkers to compensate for the absence of direct day to day employer oversight and control of their working methods.

Who should do assessments?

27   Those responsible for the assessment should be familiar with the main requirements of the Regulations and have the ability to:-

(a)   assess risks from the workstation and the kind of display screen work being done, for example, from a checklist completed by them or others;

(b)   draw upon additional sources of information on risk as appropriate;

(c)   based upon the assessment of risk, draw valid and reliable conclusions;

(d)   make a clear record of the assessment and communicate the findings to those who need to take appropriate action;

(e)   recognise their own limitations as to assessment so that further expertise can be called on if necessary.

28   Assessments can be made by health and safety personnel, or line managers with, or trained for, these abilities. It may be necessary to call in outside expertise where, for example, display screen equipment or associated components are faulty in design or use, where workstation design is complex, or where critical tasks are being performed.

29   The views of individual users about their workstations are an essential part of the assessment, as noted in paragraph 23. Employees' safety representatives should also be encouraged to play a full part in the assessment process. In particular, they should be encouraged to report any problems in display screen work that come to their attention.

Review of assessment

30   The assessment or relevant parts of it should be reviewed in the light of changes to the display screen worker population, or changes in individual capability and where there has been some significant change to the workstation such as:

(a)   a major change to software used;

(b)   a major change to the hardware (screen, keyboard, input devices etc);

(c)   a major change in workstation furniture;

(d)   a substantial increase in the amount of time required to be spent using display screen equipment;

(e)   a substantial change in other task requirements (eg more speed or accuracy);

(f)   if the workstation is relocated;

(g)   if the lighting is significantly modified.

Assessments would also need to be reviewed if research findings indicated a significant new risk, or showed that a recognised hazard should be re-evaluated.

31   Because of the varying nature and novelty of some display screen tasks, and because there is incomplete understanding of the development of chronic ill-health problems (particularly musculoskeletal ones), prediction of the nature and likelihood of problems based upon a purely objective evaluation of equipment may be difficult. It is therefore most important that employers should encourage early reporting by users of any symptoms which may be related to display screen work. The need to report and the organisational arrangements for making a report should be covered in training.

Reducing risks

32   The assessment will highlight any particular areas which may give rise for concern, and these will require further evaluation and corrective action as appropriate. The four year lead-in period for the "minimum requirements" for workstations which are not new (see paragraph 41) does **not** apply to the requirement to reduce the risk. Risks identified in the assessment must be remedied as quickly as possible. For typical applications of display screens, such as VDUs in offices, remedial action is often straightforward, for example:

(a)   *postural problems* may be overcome by simple adjustments to the workstation such as repositioning equipment or adjusting the chair. Postural problems can also indicate a need to provide reinforced training of the user (for example on correct hand position, posture, how to adjust equipment). New equipment such as a footrest or document holder may be required in some cases;

(b)   *visual problems* may also be tackled by straightforward means such as repositioning the screen or using blinds to avoid glare, placing the screen at a more comfortable viewing distance from the user, or by ensuring the screen is kept clean. In some cases, new equipment such as window blinds or more appropriate lighting may be needed;

2

(c)   *fatigue and stress* may be alleviated by correcting obvious defects in the workstation as indicated above. In addition, as in other kinds of work, good design of the task will be important. Wherever possible the task should provide users with a degree of personal control over the pace and nature of their tasks. Proper provision must be made for training, advice and information, not only on health and safety risks but also on the use of software. Further advice is given at paragraphs 31-34 of Annex A.

33   It is important to take a systematic approach to risk reduction and recognise the limitations of the basic assessment. Observed problems may reflect the interaction of several factors or may have causes that are not obvious. For example, backache may turn out to have been caused by the worker sitting in an abnormal position in order to minimise the effects of reflections on the screen. If the factors underlying a problem appear to be complex, or if simple remedial measures do not have the desired effect, it will generally be necessary to obtain expert advice on corrective action.

Sources of information and advice

34   Annex C contains a list of relevant HSE guidance documents, for example on lighting and seating, and other publications. Further advice on health problems that may be connected with display screen work could be obtained from in-house safety or occupational health departments where applicable or, if necessary, from Employment Medical Advisory Service staff in HSE (listed in your local telephone directory under "Health and Safety Executive"). Expert advice may be obtained from independent specialists in relevant professional disciplines such as ergonomics, or lighting design. Annex C includes some recent publications from relevant professional bodies.

Standards

35   Ergonomic specifications for use of display screen equipment are contained in various international, European and British standards. Further information is given at Annex A. Compliance with relevant parts of these standards will generally not only satisfy, but go beyond the requirements of the Regulations, because such standards aim to enhance performance as well as health and safety.

Regulation 3

Requirements for workstations

(1)   Every employer shall ensure that any workstation first put into service on or after 1st January 1993 which -

    (a)   (regardless of who has provided it) may be used for the purposes of his undertaking by users; or

    (b)   has been provided by him and may be used for the purposes of his undertaking by operators,

meets the requirements laid down in the Schedule to these Regulations to the extent specified in paragraph 1 thereof.

(2)   Every employer shall ensure that any workstation first put into service on or before 31st December 1992 which -

    (a)   (regardless of who provided it) may be used for the purposes of his undertaking by users; or

(b)   was provided by him and may be used for the purposes of his undertaking by operators,

meets the requirements laid down in the Schedule to these Regulations to the extent specified in paragraph 1 thereof not later than 31st December 1996.

Extent to which employers must ensure that workstations meet the requirements laid down in this Schedule

An employer shall ensure that a workstation meets the requirements laid down in this Schedule to the extent that -

(a)   those requirements relate to a component which is present in the workstation concerned;

(b)   those requirements have effect with a view to securing the health, safety and welfare of persons at work; and

(c)   the inherent characteristics of a given task make compliance with those requirements appropriate as respects the workstation concerned.

36   Regulation 3 refers to the Schedule to the Regulations which sets out minimum requirements for display screen workstations, covering the equipment, the working environment, and the interface between computer and user/operator. Figure 1 (on page 32) summarises the main requirements. Annex A contains more information on those requirements of the Schedule which call for some interpretation.

37   Regulation 3 and the Schedule must be complied with in respect of all workstations that may be used by a display screen user or operator. Where an employer decides that a particular workstation is not used by a display screen user or operator and is unlikely to be used by one in future, there is no legal need for that workstation to comply with Regulation 3 or the Schedule, though, where it is applicable, compliance will in most cases enhance performance and efficiency. Where employers have workstations that do not comply they should take steps to ensure that display screen users or operators do not use them.

They should also bear in mind their general responsibilities under the Health and Safety at Work Act to ensure health and safety of all those at work - see paragraph 42.

Application of the Schedule

38   By virtue of paragraph 1 of the Schedule, the requirements apply only in so far as:

(a)   **the components concerned (eg document holder, chair or desk) are present at the workstation.** Where a particular item is mentioned in the Schedule, this should not be interpreted as a requirement that all workstations should have one, unless risk assessment under Regulation 2 suggests the item is necessary;

(b)   **they relate to worker health, safety and welfare.** For the purposes of these Regulations, it is only necessary to comply with the detailed requirements in paragraphs 2, 3 and 4 of the Schedule if this would actively secure the health, safety or welfare of persons at work. The requirements in the Schedule do not extend to the efficiency of use of display screen equipment, workstations or software. However, these matters are covered, in addition to worker health and safety, in BS 7179 and other standards, and in international standards in preparation (see Annex A). Compliance with such standards, where they are appropriate, should enhance efficiency as well as ensuring that relevant health and safety requirements of the Schedule are also satisfied;

(c) **the inherent requirements or characteristics of the task make compliance appropriate;** for example, where the task could not be carried out successfully if all the requirements in the Schedule were complied with. [Note that it is the demands of the task, rather than the capabilities of any particular equipment, that are the deciding factor here.]

39   In practice, the detailed requirements in paragraphs 2 to 4 of the Schedule are most likely to be fully applicable in typical office situations, for example where a VDU is used for tasks such as data entry or word processing. In more specialised applications of display screens compliance with particular requirements in the Schedule may be inappropriate where there would be no benefit to, or even adverse effects on, health and safety. Where display screen equipment is used to control machinery, processes or vehicle traffic, it is clearly essential to consider the implications of any design changes for the rest of the workforce and the public, as well as the health and safety of the screen user.

40   The following examples illustrate how these factors can operate in practice. They each include a reference to the relevant part of paragraph 1 of the Schedule:

(a) where, as in some control-room applications, a screen is used from a standing position and without reference to documents, a work surface and chair may be unnecessary [Schedule 1(a)];

(b) some individuals who suffer from certain back complaints may benefit from a chair with a fixed back rest or a special chair without a back rest [Schedule 1(b)];

(c) wheelchair users work from a 'chair' that may not comply with the requirements in paragraph 2(e) of the Schedule. They may have special requirements for work surface (eg height); in practice some wheelchair users may need a purpose-built workstation but others may prefer to use existing work surfaces. Clearly the needs of the individual here should have priority over rigid compliance with paragraph 2 of the Schedule [Schedule 1(b)];

(d) where a user may need to rapidly locate and operate emergency controls, placing them on a detachable keyboard may be inappropriate [Schedule 1(b) and (c)];

(e) where there are banks of screens as in process control or air traffic control for example, individually tilting and swivelling screens may be undesirable as the screens may need to be aligned with one another and/ or be aligned for easy viewing from the operator's seat. Detachable keyboards may also be undesirable if a particular keyboard needs to be associated with a particular screen and/or instrumentation in a multi-screen array [Schedule 1 (c) and (b)];

(f) a brightness control would be inappropriate for process control screens used to display alarm signals - turning down the brightness could cause an alarm to be missed [Schedule 1 (b) and (c)];

18

(g)   screens that are necessarily close to other work equipment (for example, in a fixed assembly such as a control room panel) that needs to be well-illuminated will need carefully positioned local lighting - it may then be inappropriate for the screen to tilt and swivel as this could give rise to strong reflections on the screen [Schedule 1(b)];

(h)   where microfiche is used to keep records of original documents, screen characters may not be well-defined or clearly formed if the original was in poor condition or was badly photographed [Schedule 1(c)];

(i)   radar screens used in air traffic control have characters which have blurred "tails" and hence might be considered to be not well-defined and clearly formed; however long-persistence phosphors are deliberately used in these screens in order to indicate the direction of movement of the aircraft [Schedule 1(c)];

(j)   screens forming part of a simulator for ship or aircraft crew training may have special features that do not comply with the Schedule but are necessary if the simulator is to accurately mimic the features of the exempt display screen equipment on the ship or aircraft [Schedule 1(c)].

Transitional period for existing equipment

41   Employers are required to ensure that workstations, whether or not they are new, which are put into service in their undertakings on or after the coming into force of these Regulations comply with the Schedule where it is relevant. Workstations already in service should comply by 31 December 1996. If new display screen equipment is put into service at an existing workstation, the whole workstation concerned should be regarded as new and brought into compliance with the Schedule straight away. However, if any other part of an existing workstation is changed, only the new component need comply with the Schedule at once; the remainder of the workstation need not comply until 31 December 1996.

42   Where the Schedule does not apply, either because its requirements are not applicable (under paragraph 1) or the workstation is not new, employers must still comply with other provisions of these Regulations as well as with the Health and Safety at Work Act to ensure that risks to users and operators are reduced to the lowest extent reasonably practicable. Thus:

(a)   if assessment of an existing workstation shows there is a risk to users or operators, the employer should take immediate steps to reduce the risk; or

(b)   where paragraph 1(a) or (c) of the Schedule is applicable and the minimum requirements in paragraphs 2, 3 and 4 of the Schedule are therefore not being followed, the employer must ensure that the health and safety of users and operators are adequately safeguarded by whatever other means are appropriate, reasonably practicable and necessary.

Daily work routine of users

Every employer shall so plan the activities of users at work in his undertaking that their daily work on display screen equipment is periodically interrupted by such breaks or changes of activity as reduce their workload at that equipment.

43   In most tasks, natural breaks or pauses occur as a consequence of the inherent organisation of the work. Whenever possible, jobs at display screens should be designed to consist of a mix of screen-based and non screen-based work to prevent fatigue and to vary visual and mental demands. Where the job unavoidably contains spells of intensive display screen work (whether using the keyboard or input device, reading the screen, or a mixture of the two), these should be broken up by periods of non-intensive, non-display screen work. Where work cannot be so organised, eg in jobs requiring only data or text entry requiring sustained attention and concentration, deliberate breaks or pauses must be introduced.

Nature and timing of breaks or changes of activity

44   Where the display screen work involves intensive use of the keyboard, any activity that would demand broadly similar use of the arms or hands should be avoided during breaks. Similarly, if the display screen work is visually demanding any activities during breaks should be of a different visual character. Breaks must also allow users to vary their posture. Exercise routines which include blinking, stretching and focussing eyes on distant objects can be helpful and could be covered in training programmes.

45   It is not appropriate to lay down requirements for breaks which apply to all types of work; it is the nature and mix of demands made by the job which determine the length of break necessary to prevent fatigue. But some general guidance can be given:

(a)   breaks should be taken before the onset of fatigue, not in order to recuperate and when performance is at a maximum, before productivity reduces. The timing of the break is more important than its length;

(b)   breaks or changes of activity should be included in working time. They should reduce the workload at the screen, ie should not result in a higher pace or intensity of work on account of their introduction;

(c)   short, frequent breaks are more satisfactory than occasional, longer breaks: eg, a 5-10 minute break after 50-60 minutes continuous screen and/or keyboard work is likely to be better than a 15 minute break every 2 hours;

(d)   if possible, breaks should be taken away from the screen;

(e)   Informal breaks, that is time spent not viewing the screen (eg on other tasks), appear from study evidence to be more effective in relieving visual fatigue than formal rest breaks;

(f)   wherever practicable, users should be allowed some discretion as to how they carry out tasks; individual control over the nature and pace of work allows optimal distribution of effort over the working day.

The employer's duty to plan activities

46   The employer's duty under Regulation 4 to plan the activities of users can be satisfied by arranging things so that users are able to benefit from breaks or changes of activity, and encouraging them to do so. The duty to plan does not imply a need for the employer to draw up a precise and detailed timetable for periods of DSE work and breaks.

47   It is generally best for users to be given some discretion over when to take breaks. In such cases the employer's duty to plan activities may be satisfied by allowing an adequate degree of flexibility for the user to organise their own work. However, users given total discretion may forego breaks in favour of a shorter working day, and thus may suffer fatigue. Employers should ensure that users are given adequate information and training on the need for breaks (see paragraphs 64 and 66 below). Where users forego breaks despite this, it may be necessary for employers to lay down minimum requirements for the frequency of breaks while still allowing users some flexibility.

48   The employer's duty is to plan activities so that breaks or changes of activity are taken by users during their normal work. There are a few situations, for example where users working in a control room are handling an unforeseen emergency, where other health and safety considerations may occasionally dictate that normal breaks are not taken.

Eyes and eyesight

(1)   Where a person -

(a)   is already a user on the date of coming into force of these Regulations; or

(b)   is an employee who does not habitually use display screen equipment as a significant part of his normal work but is to become a user in the undertaking in which he is already employed,

his employer shall ensure that he is provided at his request with an appropriate eye and eyesight test, any such test to be carried out by a competent person.

(2)   Any eye and eyesight test provided in accordance with paragraph (1) shall -

(a)   in any case to which sub-paragraph (a) of that paragraph applies, be carried out as soon as practicable after being requested by the user concerned; and

(b)   in any case to which sub-paragraph (b) of that paragraph applies, be carried out before the employee concerned becomes a user.

(3)   At regular intervals after an employee has been provided with an eye and eyesight test in accordance with paragraphs (1) and (2), his employer shall, subject to paragraph (6), ensure that he is provided with a further eye and eyesight test of an appropriate nature, any such test to be carried out by a competent person.

(4)   Where a user experiences visual difficulties which may reasonably be considered to be caused by work on display screen equipment, his employer shall ensure that he is provided at his request with an appropriate eye and eyesight test, any such test to be carried out by a competent person as soon as practicable after being requested as aforesaid.

(5)   Every employer shall ensure that each user employed by him is provided with special corrective appliances appropriate for the work being done by the user concerned where -

(a)   normal corrective appliances cannot be used; and

(b)   the result of any eye and eyesight test which the user has been given in accordance with this regulation shows such provision to be necessary.

(6)   Nothing in paragraph (3) shall require an employer to provide any employee with an eye and eyesight test against that employee's will.

49   There is no reliable evidence that work with display screen equipment causes any permanent damage to eyes or eyesight, but it may make users with pre-existing vision defects more aware of them. This (and/or poor working conditions) may give some users temporary visual fatigue or headaches. Uncorrected vision defects can make work at display screens more tiring or stressful than it should be, and correcting defects can improve comfort, job satisfaction and performance. (Note that some display screen work may also require specific visual capabilities such as colour discrimination).

Eye and eyesight test

50   Regulations 5(1) and 5(2) require employers to provide users who so request it with an appropriate eye and eyesight test. In Great Britain an "appropriate eye and eyesight test" means a "sight test" as defined in the Opticians Act legislation[1]. The test includes a test of vision and an examination of the eye. For the purpose of the Display Screen Equipment Regulations, the test should take account of the nature of the users' work, including the distance at which the screen is viewed. Display screen users are not obliged to have such tests performed but where they choose to exercise their entitlement, employers should offer an examination by a registered ophthalmic optician, or a registered medical practitioner with suitable qualifications ("optometrist" and "doctor" respectively in the paragraphs below). (All registered medical practitioners, including those in company occupational health departments, are entitled to carry out sight tests but normally only those with an ophthalmic qualification do so).

51   Regulation 5(1) gives employers a duty to ensure the provision of appropriate eye and eyesight tests on request:

(a)   to their employees who are already users when the Regulations come into force;

(b)   and (thereafter) to any of their non-user employees who are to become users.

[1] S36(2) of the Opticians Act 1989 defines testing sight as "determining whether there is any and, if so, what defect of sight and of correcting, remedying or relieving any such defect of an anatomical or physiological nature by means of an optical appliance prescribed on the basis of the determination". The test is defined in further detail in the Sight Testing Examination and Prescription (No 2) Regulations 1989.

The Regulations do not give employers any duty to offer eye and eyesight tests to persons not in their employment, such as applicants for jobs. However, where somebody has been recruited and is to work with display screen equipment to the extent that they will become a user, Regulation 5(1)(b) becomes applicable. Hence where a newly recruited employee of this kind - whether or not they have been a user in any previous employment in a different undertaking - requests one, an appropriate eye and eyesight test should be arranged by their new employer. The test should be carried out before the newly recruited employee becomes a user, as required by Regulation 5(2)(b). This does not mean that new recruits must be given a test before doing any display screen work, but they would have to be given a test (if they requested one) before doing sufficient display screen work for this to be regarded as a significant part of their normal work. For guidance on what this means in practice, see paragraphs 10-13 above on the definition of a user.

52   The British College of Optometrists has produced a statement of good practice for optometrists, obtainable from them (see Annex C). Among other things, it makes clear that the purpose of the eye test by an optometrist or doctor under Regulation 5 is to decide whether the user has any defect of sight which requires correction when working with a display screen. It follows that users need to be able to describe their display screen and working environment when they have the eye test. As the College points out, the optometrist will need to make a report to the employer, copied to the employee, stating clearly whether or not a corrective appliance is needed specifically for display screen work and when re-examination should take place. Any prescription, or other confidential clinical information from the eye test, can only be provided to the employer with the employee's consent.

Vision screening tests

53   Vision screening tests are a means of identifying individuals with defective vision who need a full sight test (see paragraph 50). These tests are not designed to screen for eye defects, such as injury or disease, that may not at first affect vision. Where companies offer vision screening facilities, some users may opt for a vision screening test to check their need for a full sight test. Other users, however, may choose at the outset to exercise their entitlement to a full sight test, and in such cases the employer must arrange for the test specified in paragraph 50 to be provided.

54   Where the user opts for vision screening, the screening instrument or other test method used should be capable of testing vision at the distances appropriate to the user's display screen work, including the intermediate distance at which screens are viewed (normally 50-60 cm). Where test results indicate that vision is defective at the relevant distances, the user should be informed and referred to an optometrist or doctor for a full sight test.

55   Those conducting eyesight screening tests should have basic knowledge of the eye and its function and be competent in operation of the instrument and/or tests. Both the test results and the need for further referral should be assessed by those with medical, ophthalmic, nursing or paramedical skills.

Regularity of provision of eye and eyesight tests

56   Regulation 5 requires that eye and eyesight tests are provided:

(a)   as soon as practicable after display screen users have made a request;

(b)   for employees who are to become users, and have made a request. In such cases the test must be carried out before the employee becomes a user;

(c)   for users at regular intervals thereafter to check the need for special corrective appliances for display screen work, provided that they want the tests. Employers should be guided by the clinical judgement of the optometrist or doctor on the frequency of repeat testing. The frequency of repeat testing needed will vary between individuals, according to factors such as age. However, employers are not responsible for any corrections for vision defects or examinations for eye complaints which are not related to display screen work which may become necessary within the period. These are the responsibility of the individual concerned;

(d)   for users experiencing visual difficulties which may reasonably be considered to be related to the display screen work, for example visual symptoms such as eyestrain or focussing difficulties.

57   Where an eye test by an optometrist suggests that a user is suffering eye injury or disease, the user will be referred to his or her registered medical practitioner for further examination. This examination is free of charge under the National Health Service.

Corrective appliances

58   "Special" corrective appliances (normally spectacles) provided to meet the requirements of the Regulations will be those appliances prescribed to correct vision defects at the viewing distance or distances used specifically for the display screen work concerned. "Normal" corrective appliances are spectacles prescribed for any other purpose. It should be noted that experience has shown that in most working populations only a minority (usually less than 10%) will need special corrective appliances for display screen work. Those who need special corrective appliances may include users who already wear spectacles or contact lenses, or others who have uncorrected vision defects.

59   Anti-glare screens, and so-called "VDU spectacles" and other devices that purport to protect against radiation, are not special corrective appliances (see paragraphs 27-30 of Annex A for advice on radiation).

Employers' liability for costs

60   The provision of eye and eyesight tests and of special corrective appliances under the Regulations is at the expense of the **user's employer**. This is the case even if the user works on other employers' workstations. Employers are free to specify that users' tests and correction are provided by a particular company or professional. "Normal" corrective appliances are at the user's own expense.

61   Users needing special corrective appliances may be prescribed a special pair of spectacles for display screen work. Employers' liability for costs is restricted to payment of the cost of a basic appliance, ie of a type and quality adequate for its function. If users wish to choose more costly appliances (eg with designer frames; or lenses with optional treatments not necessary for the work), the employer is not obliged to pay for these. In these circumstances employers may either provide a basic appliance as above, or may opt to contribute a portion of the total cost of a luxury appliance equal to the cost of a basic appliance.

62   If users are permitted by their employers to choose spectacles to correct eye or vision defects for purposes which include display screen work but go wider than that, employers need contribute only the costs attributable to the requirements of the display screen work involved.

Provision of training

   (1)   Where a person -

   (a)   is already a user on the date of coming into force of these Regulations; or

   (b)   is an employee who does not habitually use display screen equipment as a significant part of his normal work but is to become a user in the undertaking in which he is already employed,

his employer shall ensure that he is provided with adequate health and safety training in the use of any workstation upon which he may be required to work.

   (2)   Every employer shall ensure that each user at work in his undertaking is provided with adequate health and safety training whenever the organisation of any workstation in that undertaking upon which he may be required to work is substantially modified.

63   In accordance with this Regulation, employers should ensure that all users who make use of their workstations or are required to use other workstations have been provided with **health and safety** training, in addition to the training received in order to do the work itself. In practice, there may be considerable overlap between general training requirements and specific health and safety ones (for example the development of keyboard skills) and they are best done together. They will then reinforce each other and facilitate efficient and effective use of the equipment as well as avoidance of risk. The purpose of training is to increase the user's competence to use workstation equipment safely and reduce the risk to their or anyone else's health. In considering the extent of any training which will be necessary in a particular case, the employer needs to make up any shortfalls between the user's existing competence and that necessary to use the equipment in a safe and healthy way. The development of specific statements of what the user needs to do and how well (ie statements of competence) will assist the employer to determine the extent of any shortfall.

64   Training will need to be adapted to the requirements of the particular display screen tasks, be adapted to users' skills and capabilities and be refreshed or updated as the hardware, software, workstation, environment or job are modified. (A workstation should be regarded as having been "substantially modified" for the purposes of Regulation 6(2) if there has been a significant change to it, as set out in paragraph 30 above). Special training or retraining needs may need to be considered for rehabilitation of people absent for long periods, particularly if ill-health problems are related to the visual, musculoskeletal or stress-related risks referred to earlier. Organisations should develop systems for identifying the occasions when any of these needs for training arise.

65   The health and safety training should be aimed at reducing or minimising the three risk areas outlined at paragraph 19 above and in Annex B, with reference to the part played by the individual user. To do this, six inter-related aspects of training should be covered:-

(a) The user's role in correct and timely detection and recognition of hazards and risks. This should cover both the absence of desirable features (chair comfort) and the presence of undesirable ones (screen reflections and glare) together with information on health risks and how problems may be manifested.

(b) A simple explanation of the causes of risk and the mechanisms by which harm may be brought about, for example poor posture leading to static loading on the musculoskeletal system and eventual fatigue and pain.

(c) User initiated actions and procedures which will bring risks under control and to acceptable levels. Training should cover the following:-

- the desirability of comfortable posture and the importance of postural change;

- the use of adjustment mechanisms on equipment, particularly furniture, so that stress and fatigue can be minimised;

- the use and arrangement of workstation components to facilitate good posture, prevent over-reaching and avoid glare and reflections on the screen;

- the need for regular cleaning (or inspection) of screens and other equipment for maintenance;

- the need to take advantage of breaks and changes of activity.

(d) Organisational arrangements by which symptoms or problems with the workstation can be communicated to management.

(e) Information on these Regulations, particularly as regards eyesight, rest pauses and the contents of Annex A.

(f) The user's contribution to assessments.

66   New users could be given such training at the same time as they are trained on how to use the equipment. The information required to be provided under Regulation 7 will reinforce the training and could usefully be in the form of posters or cards with pictorial reminders of some of the essential points. Figure 2 (on page 33) provides an example.

Provision of information

(1)   Every employer shall ensure that operators and users at work in his undertaking are provided with adequate information about -

(a)   all aspects of health and safety relating to their workstations; and

(b)   such measures taken by him in compliance with his duties under regulations 2 and 3 as relate to them and their work.

(2)   Every employer shall ensure that users at work in his undertaking are provided with adequate information about such measures taken by him in compliance with his duties under regulations 4 and 6(2) as relate to them and their work.

(3) Every employer shall ensure that users employed by him are provided with adequate information about such measures taken by him in compliance with his duties under regulations 5 and 6(1) as relate to them and their work.

67   There is a general requirement under the Management of Health and Safety at Work Regulations 1992 for employers to provide information on risks to health and safety to all their own employees as well as to employers of other employees on site, to visiting employees, and to the self-employed. Under Regulation 7 of the Display Screen Regulations specific information should be provided as follows:

		Information on:					
		Risks from display screen equipment and workstations	*Risk assessment and measures to reduce the risks (Regs 2 and 3)*	*Breaks and activity changes (Reg 4)*	*Eye and eyesight tests (Reg 5)*	*Initial training (Reg 6(1))*	*Training when workstation modified (Reg 6(2))*
DOES EMPLOYER HAVE TO PROVIDE INFORMATION TO DISPLAY SCREEN WORKERS WHO ARE:	Users employed by the undertaking	Yes	Yes	Yes	Yes	Yes	Yes
	Users employed by other employer	Yes	Yes	Yes	No	No	Yes
	Operators in the undertaking	Yes	Yes	No	No	No	No

68   The information should among other things include reminders of the measures taken to reduce the risks such as the system for reporting problems, the availability of adjustable window covering and furniture, **and of how to make use of them**. It will thus reinforce any training provided by the employer and be a useful reminder to those trained already.

Exemption certificates

(1)   The Secretary of State for Defence may, in the interests of national security, exempt any of the home forces, any visiting force or any headquarters from any of the requirements imposed by these Regulations.

(2)   Any exemption such as is specified in paragraph (1) may be granted subject to conditions and to a limit of time and may be revoked by the Secretary of State for Defence by a further certificate in writing at any time.

(3)   In this regulation -

(a) "the home forces" has the same meaning as in section 12(1) of the Visiting Forces Act 1952[a];

(b) "headquarters" has the same meaning as in article 3(2) of the Visiting Forces and International Headquarters (Application of Law) Order 1965[b]; and

(c) "visiting force" has the same meaning as it does for the purposes of any provision of Part I of the Visiting Forces Act 1952.

(a) 1952 c.7
(b) SI 1965/1536, to which there are amendments not relevant to these Regulations

Extension outside Great Britain

These Regulations shall, subject to regulation 1(4), apply to and in relation to the premises and activities outside Great Britain to which sections 1 to 59 and 80 to 82 of the Health and Safety at Work etc. Act 1974 apply by virtue of the Health and Safety at Work etc. Act 1974 (Application Outside Great Britain) Order 1989[a] as they apply within Great Britain.

(a) SI 1989/840

(Which sets out the minimum requirements for workstations which are contained in the Annex to Council Directive 90/270/EEC[a] on the minimum safety and health requirements for work with display screen equipment)

Extent to which employers must ensure that workstations meet the requirements laid down in this Schedule

1   An employer shall ensure that a workstation meets the requirements laid down in this Schedule to the extent that-

(a)   those requirements relate to a component which is present in the workstation concerned;

(b)   those requirements have effect with a view to securing the health, safety and welfare of persons at work; and

(c)   the inherent characteristics of a given task make compliance with those requirements appropriate as respects the workstation concerned.

Equipment

2   (a)   *General comment*

The use as such of the equipment must not be a source of risk for operators or users.

(b)   *Display screen*

The characters on the screen shall be well-defined and clearly formed, of adequate size and with adequate spacing between the characters and lines.

The image on the screen should be stable, with no flickering or other forms of instability.

The brightness and the contrast between the characters and the background shall be easily adjustable by the operator or user, and also be easily adjustable to ambient conditions.

The screen must swivel and tilt easily and freely to suit the needs of the operator or user.

It shall be possible to use a separate base for the screen or an adjustable table.

The screen shall be free of reflective glare and reflections liable to cause discomfort to the operator or user.

(c)   *Keyboard*

The keyboard shall be tiltable and separate from the screen so as to allow the operator or user to find a comfortable working position avoiding fatigue in the arms or hands.

The space in front of the keyboard shall be sufficient to provide support for the hands and arms of the operator or user.

(a) OJ No L156, 21.6.90, p.14

The keyboard shall have a matt surface to avoid reflective glare.

The arrangement of the keyboard and the characteristics of the keys shall be such as to facilitate the use of the keyboard.

The symbols on the keys shall be adequately contrasted and legible from the design working position.

(d) ***Work desk or work surface***

The work desk or work surface shall have a sufficiently large, low-reflectance surface and allow a flexible arrangement of the screen, keyboard, documents and related equipment.

The document holder shall be stable and adjustable and shall be positioned so as to minimise the need for uncomfortable head and eye movements.

There shall be adequate space for operators or users to find a comfortable position.

(e) ***Work chair***

The work chair shall be stable and allow the operator or user easy freedom of movement and a comfortable position.

The seat shall be adjustable in height.

The seat back shall be adjustable in both height and tilt.

A footrest shall be made available to any operator or user who wishes one.

Environment

3   (a) ***Space requirements***

The workstation shall be dimensioned and designed so as to provide sufficient space for the operator or user to change position and vary movements.

(b) ***Lighting***

Any room lighting or task lighting provided shall ensure satisfactory lighting conditions and an appropriate contrast between the screen and the background environment, taking into account the type of work and the vision requirements of the operator or user.

Possible disturbing glare and reflections on the screen or other equipment shall be prevented by co-ordinating workplace and workstation layout with the positioning and technical characteristics of the artificial light sources.

(c) ***Reflections and glare***

Workstations shall be so designed that sources of light, such as windows and other openings, transparent or translucid walls, and brightly coloured fixtures or walls cause no direct glare and no distracting reflections on the screen.

Windows shall be fitted with a suitable system of adjustable covering to attenuate the daylight that falls on the workstation.

(d) ***Noise***

Noise emitted by equipment belonging to any workstation shall be taken into account when a workstation is being equipped, with a view in particular to ensuring that attention is not distracted and speech is not disturbed.

(e) ***Heat***

Equipment belonging to any workstation shall not produce excess heat which could cause discomfort to operators or users.

(f) ***Radiation***

All radiation with the exception of the visible part of the electromagnetic spectrum shall be reduced to negligible levels from the point of view of the protection of operators' or users' health and safety.

(g) ***Humidity***

An adequate level of humidity shall be established and maintained.

Interface between computer and operator/user

4   In designing, selecting, commissioning and modifying software, and in designing tasks using display screen equipment, the employer shall take into account the following principles:

(a)   software must be suitable for the task;

(b)   software must be easy to use and, where appropriate, adaptable to the level of knowledge or experience of the operator or user; no quantitative or qualitative checking facility may be used without the knowledge of the operators or users;

(c)   systems must provide feedback to operators or users on the performance of those systems;

(d)   systems must display information in a format and at a pace which are adapted to operators or users;

(e)   the principles of software ergonomics must be applied, in particular to human data processing.

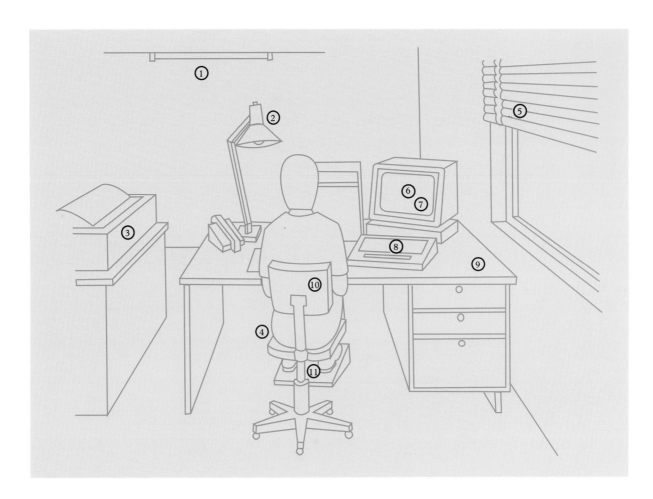

FIGURE 1

SUBJECTS DEALT WITH IN THE SCHEDULE

① ADEQUATE LIGHTING

② ADEQUATE CONTRAST, NO GLARE OR DISTRACTING REFLECTIONS

③ DISTRACTING NOISE MINIMISED

④ LEG ROOM AND CLEARANCES TO ALLOW POSTURAL CHANGES

⑤ WINDOW COVERING

⑥ SOFTWARE: APPROPRIATE TO TASK, ADAPTED TO USER, PROVIDES FEEDBACK ON SYSTEM STATUS, NO UNDISCLOSED MONITORING

⑦ SCREEN: STABLE IMAGE, ADJUSTABLE, READABLE, GLARE/REFLECTION FREE

⑧ KEYBOARD: USABLE, ADJUSTABLE, DETACHABLE, LEGIBLE

⑨ WORK SURFACE: ALLOW FLEXIBLE ARRANGEMENTS, SPACIOUS, GLARE FREE

⑩ WORK CHAIR: ADJUSTABLE

⑪ FOOTREST

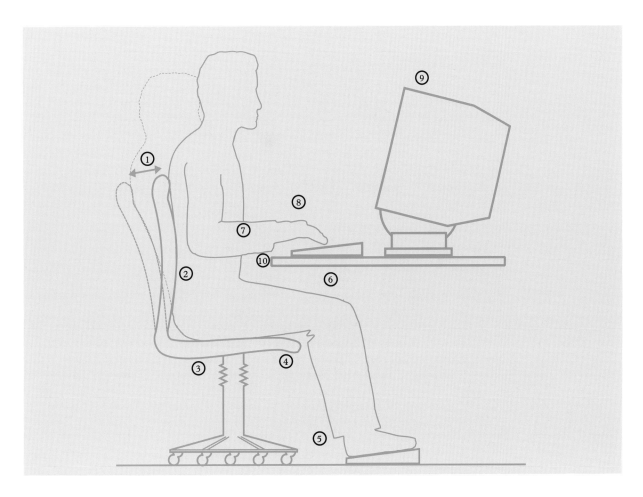

FIGURE 2

SEATING AND POSTURE FOR TYPICAL OFFICE TASKS

①   SEAT BACK ADJUSTABILITY

②   GOOD LUMBAR SUPPORT

③   SEAT HEIGHT ADJUSTABILITY

④   NO EXCESS PRESSURE ON UNDERSIDE OF THIGHS AND BACKS OF KNEES

⑤   FOOT SUPPORT IF NEEDED

⑥   SPACE FOR POSTURAL CHANGE, NO OBSTACLES UNDER DESK

⑦   FOREARMS APPROXIMATELY HORIZONTAL

⑧   MINIMAL EXTENSION, FLEXION OR DEVIATION OF WRISTS

⑨   SCREEN HEIGHT AND ANGLE SHOULD ALLOW COMFORTABLE HEAD POSITION

⑩   SPACE IN FRONT OF KEYBOARD TO SUPPORT HANDS/WRISTS DURING PAUSES IN KEYING

Annex A
Guidance on workstation minimum requirements

1   The Schedule to the Regulations sets out minimum requirements for workstations, applicable mainly to typical office workstations. As explained in the guidance (paragraph 38) these requirements are applicable only in so far as the components referred to are present at the workstation concerned, the requirements are not precluded by the inherent requirements of the task, and the requirements relate to worker health, safety and welfare. Paragraphs 39-40 give examples of situations in which some aspects of these minimum requirements would not apply.

2   The requirements of the Schedule are in most cases self-explanatory but particular points to note are covered below.

General approach: use of standards

3   Ergonomic requirements for the use of visual display units in office tasks are contained in BS 7179. There is no requirement in the Display Screen Regulations to comply with this or any other standard. Other approaches to meeting the minimum requirements in the Regulations are possible, and may have to be adopted if special requirements of the task or needs of the user preclude the use of equipment made to relevant standards. However, employers may find standards helpful as workstations satisfying BS 7179, or forthcoming international standards (see below), would meet and in most cases go beyond the minimum requirements in the Schedule to the Regulations.

4   BS 7179 is a six-part interim standard covering the ergonomics of design and use of visual display terminals in offices; it is concerned with the efficient use of VDUs as well as with user health, safety and comfort. BS 7179 has been issued by the British Standards Institution in recognition of industry's immediate need for guidance and is intended for the managers and supervisors of VDU users as well as for equipment manufacturers. While originally confined to office VDU tasks, many of the general ergonomic recommendations in BS 7179 will be relevant to some non-office situations.

5   International standards are in preparation that will cover the same subject in an expanded form. BS 7179 will be withdrawn when the European standards organisation CEN (Comité Européen de Normalisation) issues its multipart standard (EN 29241) concerned with the ergonomics of design and use of visual display terminals for office tasks. This CEN Standard will in turn be based on an ISO Standard (ISO 9241) that is currently being developed. The eventual ISO and CEN standards will cover screen and keyboard design and evaluation, workstation design and environmental requirements, non-keyboard input devices and ergonomic requirements for software design and usability. While the CEN standard is not formally linked to the Display Screen Equipment directive, one of its aims is to establish appropriate levels of user health and safety and comfort. Technical data in the various parts of the CEN standard (and currently BS 7179) may therefore help employers to meet the requirements laid down in the Schedule to the Regulations.

6   There are other standards that deal with requirements for furniture, some of which are cross-referenced by BS 7179. These include BS 3044, which is a guide to ergonomic principles in the design and selection of office furniture generally. There is also now a separate standardisation initiative within CEN concerned with the performance requirements for office furniture, including dimensioning appropriate for European user populations. Details of relevant British, European and international standards can be obtained from the Department of Trade and Industry - see Annex C.

7   Other more detailed and stringent standards are relevant to certain specialised applications of display screens, especially those where the health or safety of persons other than the screen user may be affected. Some examples in particular subject areas are:-

(1) *Process control*

A large number of British and international standards are or will be relevant to the design of display screen interfaces for use in process control - such as the draft Standard ISO 11064 on the general ergonomic design of control rooms.

(2) *Applications with machinery safety implications*

Draft Standard pr EN 614 pt 1 - Ergonomic design principles in safety of machinery.

(3) *Safety of programmable electronic systems*

Draft document IEC 65A (Secretariat) 122 Draft: Functional safety of electrical/electronic programmable systems.

Applications such as these are outside the scope of these guidance notes. Anyone involved in the design of such display screen interfaces and others where there may be safety considerations for non-users should seek appropriate specialist advice. Many relevant standards are listed in the DTI publication *Directory of HCI Standards* - see Annex C.

Equipment

Display screen

8   Choice of display screen should be considered in relation to other elements of the work system, such as the type and amount of information required for the task, and environmental factors. A satisfactory display can be achieved by custom design for a specific task or environment, or by appropriate adjustments to adapt the display to suit changing requirements or environmental conditions.

Display stability

9   Individual perceptions of screen flicker vary and a screen which is flicker-free to 90% of users should be regarded as satisfying the minimum requirement. (It is not technically feasible to eliminate flicker for all users). A change to a different display can resolve individual problems with flicker. Persistent display instabilities - flicker, jump, jitter or swim - may indicate basic design problems and assistance should be sought from suppliers.

Brightness and contrast

10   Negative or positive image polarity (light characters on a dark background, dark characters on a light background respectively) is acceptable, and each has different advantages. With negative polarity flicker is less perceptible, legibility is better for those with low acuity vision, and characters may be perceived as larger than they are; with positive polarity, reflections are less perceptible, edges appear sharper and luminance balance is easier to achieve.

11   It is important for the brightness and contrast of the display to be appropriate for ambient lighting conditions; trade-offs between character brightness and sharpness may be needed to achieve an acceptable balance. In many kinds of equipment this is achieved by providing a control or controls which allow the user to make adjustments.

Screen adjustability

12   Adjustment mechanisms allow the screen to be tilted or swivelled to avoid glare and reflections and enable the worker to maintain a natural and relaxed posture. They may be built into the screen, form part of the workstation furniture or be provided by separate screen support devices; they should be simple and easy to operate. Screen height adjustment devices, although not essential, may be a useful means of adjusting the screen to the correct height for the worker. (The reference in the Schedule to adjustable tables does not mean these have to be provided).

Glare and reflections

13   Screens are generally manufactured without highly reflective surface finishes but in adverse lighting conditions, reflection and glare may be a problem. Advice on lighting is below (paragraphs 20-24).

Keyboard

14   Keyboard design should allow workers to locate and activate keys quickly, accurately and without discomfort. The choice of keyboard will be dictated by the nature of the task and determined in relation to other elements of the work system. Hand support may be incorporated into the keyboard for support while keying or at rest depending on what the worker finds comfortable, may be provided in the form of a space between the keyboard and front edge of the desk, or may be given by a separate hand/wrist support attached to the work surface.

Work desk or work surface

15   Work surface dimensions may need to be larger than for conventional non-screen office work, to take adequate account of:

(a)   the range of tasks performed (eg screen viewing, keyboard input, use of other input devices, writing on paper etc);

(b)   position and use of hands for each task;

(c)   use and storage of working materials and equipment (documents, telephones etc).

16   Document holders are useful for work with hard copy, particularly for workers who have difficulty in refocussing. They should position working documents at a height, visual plane and, where appropriate, viewing distance similar to those of the screen; be of low reflectance; be stable; and not reduce the readability of source documents.

Work chair

17   The primary requirement here is that the work chair should allow the user to achieve a comfortable position. Seat height adjustments should accommodate the needs of users for the tasks performed. The Schedule requires the seat to be adjustable in height (ie relative to the ground) and the

seat back to be adjustable in height (also relative to the ground) and tilt. Provided the chair design meets these requirements and allows the user to achieve a comfortable posture, it is not necessary for the height or tilt of the seat back to be adjustable independently of the seat. Automatic backrest adjustments are acceptable if they provide adequate back support. General health and safety advice and specifications for seating are given in the HSE publication *Seating at Work* (HS(G)57). A range of publications with detailed advice covering comfort and performance as well as health and safety is included in Annex C.

18   Footrests may be necessary where individual workers are unable to rest their feet flat on the floor (eg where work surfaces cannot be adjusted to the right height in relation to other components of the workstation). Footrests should not be used when they are not necessary as this can result in poor posture.

Environment

Space requirements

19   Prolonged sitting in a static position can be harmful. It is most important that support surfaces for display screen and other equipment and materials used at the workstation should allow adequate clearance for postural changes. This means adequate clearances for thighs, knees, lower legs and feet under the work surface and between furniture components. The height of the work surface should allow a comfortable position for the arms and wrists, if a keyboard is used.

Lighting, reflections and glare

20   Lighting should be appropriate for all the tasks performed at the workstation, eg reading from the screen, keyboard work, reading printed text, writing on paper etc. General lighting - by artificial or natural light, or a combination - should illuminate the entire room to an adequate standard. Any supplementary individual lighting provided to cater for personal needs or a particular task should not adversely affect visual conditions at nearby workstations.

Illuminance

21   High illuminances render screen characters less easy to see but improve the ease of reading documents. Where a high illuminance environment is preferred for this or other reasons, the use of positive polarity screens (dark characters on a light background) has advantages as these can be used comfortably at higher illuminances than can negative polarity screens.

Reflections and glare

22   Problems which can lead to visual fatigue and stress can arise for example from unshielded bright lights or bright areas in the worker's field of view; from an imbalance between brightly and dimly lit parts of the environment; and from reflections on the screen or other parts of the workstation.

23   Measures to minimise these problems include: shielding, replacing or repositioning sources of light; rearranging or moving work surfaces, documents or all or parts of workstations; modifying the colour or reflectance of walls, ceilings, furnishings etc near the workstation; altering the intensity of vertical to horizontal illuminance; or a combination of these. Anti-glare screen filters should be considered as a last resort if other measures fail to solve the problem.

24   General guidance on minimum lighting standards necessary to ensure health and safety of workplaces is available in the HSE guidance note *Lighting at Work* (HS(G)38). This does not cover ways of using lighting to maximise task performance or enhance the appearance of the workplace, although it does contain a bibliography listing relevant publications in this area. Specific and detailed guidance is given in the CIBSE Lighting Guide 3 *Lighting for visual display terminals*. Full details of these publications are given in Annex C.

Noise

25   Noise from equipment such as printers at display screen workstations should be kept to levels which do not impair concentration or prevent normal conversation (unless the noise is designed to attract attention, eg to warn of a malfunction). Noise can be reduced by replacement, sound-proofing or repositioning of the equipment; sound insulating partitions between noisy equipment and the rest of the workstation are an alternative.

Heat and humidity

26   Electronic equipment can be a source of dry heat which can modify the thermal environment at the workstation. Ventilation and humidity should be maintained at levels which prevent discomfort and problems of sore eyes.

Radiation

27   The Schedule requires radiation with the exception of the visible part of the electromagnetic spectrum (ie visible light) to be reduced to negligible levels from the point of view of the protection of users' health and safety. In fact so little radiation is emitted from current designs of display screen equipment that no special action is necessary to meet this requirement (see also Annex B, paragraphs 8-10).

28   Taking cathode ray tube displays as an example, ionising radiation is emitted only in exceedingly small quantities, so small as to be generally much less than the natural background level to which everyone is exposed. Emissions of ultraviolet, visible and infrared radiation are also very small, and workers will receive much less than the maximum exposures generally recommended by national and international advisory bodies.

29   For radio frequencies, the exposures will also be well below the maximum values generally recommended by national and international advisory bodies for health protection purposes. The levels of electric and magnetic fields are similar to those from common domestic electrical devices. Although much research has been carried out on possible health effects from exposure to electromagnetic radiation, no adverse health effects have been shown to result from the emissions from display screen equipment.

30   Thus it is not necessary, from the standpoint of limiting risk to human health, for employers or workers to take any action to reduce radiation levels or to attempt to measure emissions; in fact the latter is not recommended as meaningful interpretation of the data is very difficult. There is no need for users to be given protective devices such as anti-radiation screens.

Task design and software

Principles of task design

31   Inappropriate task design can be among the causes of stress at work. Stress jeopardises employee motivation, effectiveness and efficiency and in

some cases it can lead to significant health problems. The Regulations are only applicable where health and safety rather than productivity is being put at risk; but employers may find it useful to consider both aspects together as task design changes put into effect for productivity reasons may also benefit health, and vice versa.

32　In display screen work, good design of the task can be as important as the correct choice of equipment, furniture and working environment. It is advantageous to:

(a)　design jobs in a way that offers users variety, opportunities to exercise discretion, opportunities for learning, and appropriate feedback, in preference to simple repetitive tasks whenever possible. (For example, the work of a typist can be made less repetitive and stressful if an element of clerical work is added);

(b)　match staffing levels to volumes of work, so that individual users are not subject to stress through being either overworked or underworked;

(c)　allow users to participate in the planning, design and implementation of work tasks whenever possible.

Principles of software ergonomics

33　In most display screen work the software controls both the presentation of information on the screen and the ways in which the worker can manipulate the information. Thus software design can be an important element of task design. Software that is badly designed or inappropriate for the task will impede the efficient completion of the work and in some cases may cause sufficient stress to affect the health of a user. Involving a sample of users in the purchase or design of software can help to avoid problems.

34　Detailed ergonomic standards for software are likely to be developed in future as part of the ISO 9241 standard; for the moment, the Schedule lists a few general principles which employers should take into account. Requirements of the organisation and of display screen workers should be established as the basis for designing, selecting, and modifying software. In many (though not all) applications the main points are:

Suitability for the task

-　Software should enable workers to complete the task efficiently, without presenting unnecessary problems or obstacles.

Ease of use and adaptability

-　Workers should be able to feel that they can master the system and use it effectively following appropriate training;

-　The dialogue between the system and the worker should be appropriate for the worker's ability;

-　Where appropriate, software should enable workers to adapt the user interface to suit their ability level and preferences;

-　The software should protect workers from the consequences of errors, for example by providing appropriate warnings and information and by enabling "lost" data to be recovered wherever practicable.

Feedback on system performance

- The system should provide appropriate feedback, which may include error messages; suitable assistance ("help") to workers on request; and messages about changes in the system such as malfunctions or overloading;

- Feedback messages should be presented at the right time and in an appropriate style and format. They should not contain unnecessary information.

Format and pace

- Speed of response to commands and instructions should be appropriate to the task and to workers' abilities;

- Characters, cursor movements and position changes should where possible be shown on the screen as soon as they are input.

Performance monitoring facilities

- Quantitative or qualitative checking facilities built into the software can lead to stress if they have adverse results such as an over-emphasis on output speed;

- It is possible to design monitoring systems that avoid these drawbacks and provide information that is helpful to workers as well as managers. However, in all cases workers should be kept informed about the introduction and operation of such systems.

Display screen equipment: possible effects on health

The main hazards

1   The introduction of VDUs and other display screen equipment has been associated with a range of symptoms related to the visual system and working posture. These often reflect bodily fatigue. They can readily be prevented by applying ergonomic principles to the design, selection and installation of display screen equipment, the design of the workplace, and the organisation of the task.

Upper limb pains and discomfort

2   A range of conditions of the arm, hand and shoulder areas linked to work activities are now described as work related upper limb disorders. These range from temporary fatigue or soreness in the limb to chronic soft tissue disorders like peritendinitis or carpal tunnel syndrome. Some keyboard operators have suffered occupational cramp.

3   The contribution to the onset of any disorder of individual risk factors (eg keying rates) is not clear. It is likely that a combination of factors are concerned. Prolonged static posture of the back, neck and head are known to cause musculoskeletal problems. Awkward positioning of the hands and wrist (eg as a result of poor working technique or inappropriate work height) are further likely factors. Outbreaks of soft tissue disorders among keyboard workers have often been associated with high workloads combined with tight deadlines. This variety of factors contributing to display screen work risk requires a risk reduction strategy which embraces proper equipment, furniture, training, job design and work planning.

Eye and eyesight effects

4   Medical evidence shows that using display screen equipment is not associated with damage to eyes or eyesight; nor does it make existing defects worse. But some workers may experience **temporary** visual fatigue, leading to a range of symptoms such as impaired visual performance, red or sore eyes and headaches, or the adoption of awkward posture which can cause further discomfort in the limb. These may be caused by:

(a)   staying in the same position and concentrating for a long time;

(b)   poor positioning of the display screen equipment;

(c)   poor legibility of the screen or source documents;

(d)   poor lighting, including glare and reflections;

(e)   a drifting, flickering or jittering image on the screen.

Like other visually demanding tasks, VDU work does not cause eye damage but it may make workers with pre-existing vision defects more aware of them. Such uncorrected defects can make work with a display screen more tiring or stressful than would otherwise be the case.

Fatigue and stress

5   Many symptoms described by display screen workers reflect stresses arising from their task. They may be secondary to upper limb or visual problems but they are more likely to be caused by poor job design or work organisation, particularly lack of sufficient control of the work by the user, under-utilisation of skills, high-speed repetitive working or social isolation. All these have been linked with stress in display screen work, although clearly they are not unique to it; but attributing individual symptoms to particular aspects of a job or workplace can be difficult. The risks of display screen workers experiencing physical fatigue and stress can be minimised, however, by following the principles underlying the Display Screen Equipment Regulations 1992 and guidance, ie by careful design, selection and disposition of display screen equipment; good design of the user's workplace, environment and task; and training, consultation and involvement of the user.

Other concerns

Epilepsy

6   Display screen equipment has not been known to induce epileptic seizures. People suffering from the very rare (1 in 10 000 population) photosensitive epilepsy who react adversely to flickering lights and patterns also find they can safely work with display screens. People with epilepsy who are concerned about display screen work can seek further advice from local offices of the Employment Medical Advisory Service.

Facial dermatitis

7   Some VDU users have reported facial skin complaints such as occasional itching or reddened skin on the face and/or neck. These complaints are relatively rare and the limited evidence available suggests they may be associated with environmental factors, such as low relative humidity or static electricity near the VDU.

Electro magnetic radiation

8   Anxiety about radiation emissions from display screen equipment and possible effects on pregnant women has been widespread. However, there is substantial evidence that these concerns are unfounded. The Health and Safety Executive has consulted the National Radiological Protection Board, which has the statutory function of providing information and advice on all radiation matters to Government Departments, and the advice below summarises scientific understanding.

9   The levels of ionising and non-ionising electromagnetic radiation which are likely to be generated by display screen equipment are well below those set out in international recommendations for limiting risk to human health created by such emissions and the National Radiological Protection Board does not consider such levels to pose a significant risk to health. No special protective measures are therefore needed to protect the health of people from this radiation.

Effects on pregnant women

10   There has been considerable public concern about reports of higher levels of miscarriage and birth defects among some groups of visual display unit (VDU) workers in particular due to electromagnetic radiation. Many scientific studies have been carried out, but taken as a whole their results do

not show any link between miscarriages or birth defects and working with VDUs. Research and reviews of the scientific evidence will continue to be undertaken.

11 In the light of the scientific evidence pregnant women do not need to stop work with VDUs. However, to avoid problems caused by stress and anxiety, women who are pregnant or planning children and worried about working with VDUs should be given the opportunity to discuss their concerns with someone adequately informed of current authoritative scientific information and advice.

Further sources of information

HSE Publications

Working with VDUs IND(G) 36L 1992. Free from HSE Information Centre

HSE will also be publishing supplementary practical advice which will be available in 1993

Ergonomics at work IND(G)90L 1990. Free from HSE Information Centre

Human Factors in Industrial Safety HS(G)48 HMSO 1989
ISBN 0 11 885486 0

Seating at Work HS(G)57 1991 HMSO ISBN 0 11 885431 3

Lighting at Work HS(G)38 1987 HMSO ISBN 0 11 883964 0

Work-related Upper Limb Disorders: a guide to prevention HS(G)60 1990 HMSO
ISBN 0 11 885565 4

Lighten the Load awareness campaign on musculoskeletal disorders. Campaign pack available from Health Operations Branch, Field Operations Division, HSE, Daniel House, Trinity Road, Bootle, Merseyside L20 7HE.

Standards

British Standards Institution

Ergonomics of design and use of visual display terminals (VDTs) in offices BS 7179

Part 1 (1990) *Introduction* ISBN 0 580 18002 6

Part 2 (1990) *Recommendations for the design of office VDT tasks*
ISBN 0 580 18003 4

Part 3 (1990) *Specification for visual displays* ISBN 0 580 18008 5

Part 4 (1990) *Specification for keyboards* ISBN 0 580 18007 7

Part 5 (1990) *Specification for VDT workstations* ISBN 0 580 18009 3

Part 6 (1990) *Code of practice for the design of VDT work environments*
ISBN 0 580 18004 2

A DTI publication *Usability Now - HCI Standards and Regulations* gives a compilation of all the relevant Standards in the ergonomics field and other related areas. It is available free of charge from the *Usability Now* enquiry point on 0509 264083.

Other Publications

Guidance on Standards: Guidance as to restrictions on exposures to time varying electromagnetic fields and the 1988 recommendations of the International Non-Ionising Radiation Committee NRPB GS11 National Radiological Protection Board 1989 HMSO ISBN 0 85951314 9.

Lighting Guide. Areas for Visual Display Units (LG3: 1989) Chartered Institute of Building Services Engineers, London 1989 ISBN 0 900953 41 1

Damodaran L, Simpson A and Wilson P *Designing Systems for People* NCC Publications, The National Computing Centre Ltd, Oxford Road, Manchester 1980 ISBN 0 85012242 2

Introducing the Visual Display Unit to the Office. Available from the Business Equipment Trade Association (now the Association of Electronics Telecommunications and Business Equipment Industries), tel: 071 331 2030

Trade union guidance

The TUC and several trade unions have produced detailed publications on a wide variety of display screen work, in some cases specific to particular occupations.

Sources of expertise

Ergonomics Society

Devonshire House, Devonshire Square, Loughborough, LE11 3DW.

British College of Optometrists

10 Knaresborough Place, London SW5 0TG, tel: 071 835 1302. The College is the examining and professional body for optometrists; a registered charity run for public benefit. The College have issued *Work with display screen equipment. Statement of good practice issued by the British College of Optometrists*; this is available from them.

The Association of Optometrists

233 Blackfriars Road, London SE1 8NW, tel: 071 261 9661. The Association has issued a guide *Visual aspects of VDU usage,* available from the offices of the Association.

Chartered Institution of Building Services Engineers (CIBSE)

222 Balham High Road, London SW12 9BS.

HSE's Employment Medical Advisory Service

HSE area offices

Printed in the United Kingdom for HSE, published by HMSO   C350   2/93